Stories For Me, By

Sleeping In My Own Bed

Written by: Emily Corrice, MS, OTR/L

Illustrated by: Jessica Kelly

PUBLISHED BY
PIONEER PUBLISHING

ISBN: 978-1-957377-06-3

This book belongs to:

_____

Preface

Stories For Me, By Me is a series of books written and designed by an Occupational Therapist. These stories aim to assist families in helping their children tackle everyday, emotionally triggering activities, as well as introducing upcoming transitions and events in their children's lives. These stories take into consideration sensory, emotional, social, and behavioral components associated with tasks that may seem to be "simple" everyday activities, but pose challenges to some children. These stories can be helpful regulation tools that offer simple strategies and easy-to-understand solutions for children struggling to participate and thrive in expected activities and routines.

The second half of these stories include coloring pages with open storylines, allowing children, parents, and therapy teams to create their own personalized stories. Children can color the pictures to best resemble themselves and their environments. Parents and therapy teams can assist the children in creating a storyline, which would be most helpful for the children and their families. The back-to-back stories create repetition and consistency, helping the child to become comfortable with the activities at hand.

This book series is not intended to "fix" the challenges concerning the activity presented in the story. The stories within this series can be used as tools to supplement and assist in achieving the ultimate goal of improved participation for your child. If your child is part of a therapy team, always consult your child's therapist for best strategies and tools to assist in everyday functioning.

Stories For Me, By Me

Sleeping In My Own Bed

Soon it will be bedtime.

Bedtime means I will sleep in my own bed.

Sometimes I don't want to sleep in my own bed,
because it means I have to leave mommy and daddy.

Before bedtime, mommy and daddy
will help me take a warm bath.

This will help me relax.

After my bath, mommy and daddy will rub lotion on my hands and feet.

They will give my hands and feet big squeezes.

This will help me feel calm.

Next, I will put on my warm pajamas.

Mommy and daddy even let me wear special bedtime slippers to keep my feet nice and warm.

This will make me feel happy.

We will turn on my special bedtime light so I do not feel scared of the dark.

It lights up my room and looks so nice.

This will help me feel safe.

Next, mommy and daddy will wrap me up in a soft blanket and read me a book.

This will help me relax.

I will get really sleepy and be ready for bed.

I will hug my favorite stuffed animal while I fall asleep in my own bed.

Mommy and daddy will kiss me goodnight.

They sleep in their own bed while I sleep in my own bed.

Before I know it, it is morning time.

I slept in my own bed all night and mommy and daddy are so proud of me!

Sleeping In My Own Bed
Coloring Pages

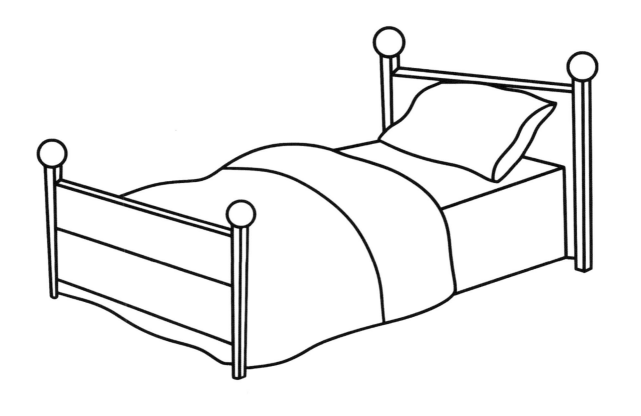

_____

_____

_____

_____

_____

_____

_____

_____

_____

_____

_____

_____

_____

_____

_____

_____

_____

_____

_____

_____

_____

_____

_____

_____

Notes for therapy teams and families:

_____

_____

_____

_____

_____

_____

_____

Check out other books in this series

Stories For Me, By Me

All books in this series are available in girl and boy editions.

Getting A Haircut

Riding The School Bus

Going To The Doctor

Trying A New Food

Washing My Hair

Printed in Great Britain
by Amazon

41793615R00021